Latino Songs
PLAYALONG!
FOR CLARINET

Ten hit songs in melody line arrangements
by Barrie Carson Turner

Chester Music
8/9 Frith Street London W1D 3JB

This book © Copyright 2001 Chester Music
ISBN 0-7119-8327-5
Order No. CH61775
Music processed by Enigma Music
Cover design by Chloë Alexander
Printed in the United Kingdom

Practice points

Each book in the *Applause* series includes suggestions – 'practice points' –
on the practice and performance of the pieces in the book.

Each piece has its own list of practice points and exercises to help you in your study of
the music. All the exercises, unless we tell you otherwise, follow a set routine.
The music is first played for you by our soloist, and then you repeat the music a second
and a third time. Metronome clicks introduce each exercise and continue throughout the music
without a break, for all three repetitions, to help you maintain the beat.
Where helpful, the exercises are slower than the music on the recording.

We hope you will find the practice points useful.

1 Bésame Mucho

• This music should be smooth and flowing.
• Enjoy the rhythmically relaxed feel of the crotchet triplets.

Exercise 1, bars 10 – 17, is taken from the opening of the melody. Take care with the triplets. The music begins
after four crotchet clicks. Listen first as we play, then you repeat the music twice.

Exercise 1 (CD Track 22)

Exercise 2, bars 42 – 49, is taken from the second part of the melody. The music begins after four crotchet
clicks.

Exercise 2 (CD Track 23)

• Be aware of the juxtaposition of the crotchet triplet with the crotchet/ two quaver rhythm that occurs in bars
42, 43, 46 and 47. The two rhythms should not be identical.
• Bars 26 – 37 are a repeat of bars 10 – 21. Knowing where the music repeats saves you practice time.
• This is a good piece in which to practise your *legato* playing.

2 Guantanamera

- Rests divide many of the phrases in this music. Be sure to count these accurately.
- The music of this piece should be quiet and dreamy.

Exercise 1, bars 5 – 12, introduces you to the opening bars of the melody. The music begins after four crotchet clicks. Listen first as we play, then you repeat the music twice.

Exercise 1 (CD Track 24)

Exercise 2, bars 12 – 20, is taken from the second half of the melody. The music begins after three crotchet clicks.

Exercise 2 (CD Track 25)

- Add a *crescendo* to the run-up leading to the change of key in bar 53.

3 Tequila

- Like much Latin American music, this piece relies heavily on syncopation for its rhythmic drive. Add your own accents to reinforce the syncopation where you feel they are appropriate.
- This piece is in 2/2 time, but count four quick crotchet beats per bar if you prefer, as we do in the exercises.

Exercise 1, bars 4 – 12, is taken from the first part of the melody. The music begins after four crotchet clicks. Listen first as we play, then you repeat the music twice.

Exercise 1 (CD Track 26)

Exercise 2, bars 20 – 28, is taken from the 'middle 8' of the music. Notice the opening phrase is repeated three times. The music begins after three crotchet clicks.

Exercise 2 (CD Track 27)

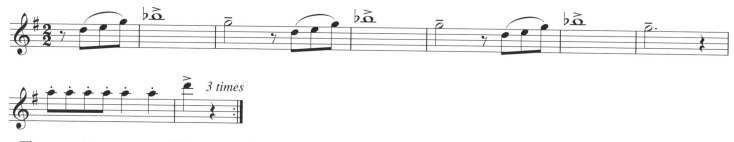

• The repetitive nature of this music should enable you to learn this piece fairly easily.

4 Guaglione

• This is a very rhythmical piece. The *staccato* notes should be played crisply.
• Count quick four as you play.

This piece is made up of four different melodies. Exercise 1, bars 20 – 28 is taken from the closing bars of the second tune. The music begins after two crotchet clicks. Listen first as we play, then you repeat the music twice.

Exercise 1 (CD Track 28)

Exercise 2, bars 36 – 43, is taken from the fourth melody of the piece. Notice the change of key. The music begins after two crotchet clicks.

Exercise 2 (CD Track 29)

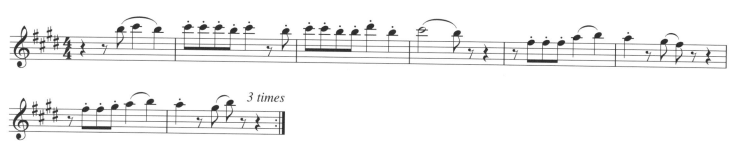

• Don't miss the change of key in bar 37. The original key returns in bar 49.
• Much of this music is repeated. Bars 63 – 69 are a repeat of 5 – 11. The first six bars of the coda similarly repeat 5 – 10. Knowing where the music repeats will save you practice time!
• The cue notes at the end are optional.

5

5 Mas Que Nada

- This piece is in 2/2 time, but count four quick crotchet beats per bar if you prefer, as we do in the exercises.
- The contrast of *staccato* and *legato* is important.

Exercise 1, bars 24 – 31, is taken from the beginning of the main melody. The music is slightly slower than the recording, and begins after five crotchet beats. Notice the frequent accented notes. Listen first as we play, then you repeat the music twice.

Exercise 1 (CD Track 30)

The music for exercise 2, bars 32 – 39, is taken from the second half of the main melody, and begins after two crotchet clicks. The music is again slightly slower than the recording.

Exercise 2 (CD Track 31)

- The music of this song is rhythmically fairly difficult. Pay particular attention to the quaver – crotchet – quaver rhythms that regularly feature here. Spend some time practising the music slowly.
- If you find yourself tripping over the tied notes, play the music first without them. When you can play the notes confidently, reinstate the ties.

6 Mambo No. 5

- The melody of this song revolves around very few notes. Much of the interest of the piece lies in the rhythms and syncopation. Add your own accents and *staccatos* where you feel they are appropriate.
- Play pairs of quavers throughout as dotted rhythms.

Exercise 1, bars 5 – 12, is taken from the opening bars of the song. The music begins after four crotchet clicks. Listen first as we play, then you repeat the music twice.

Exercise 1 (CD Track 32)

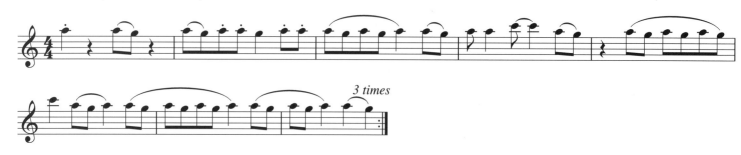

Exercise 2, bars 28 – 36, is taken from the beginning of the chorus. The music begins after two crotchet clicks.

Exercise 2 (CD Track 33)

7 Desafinado (Slightly Out Of Tune)

• Play this music lightly, and with a bounce.
• Experiment with 'relaxing' some of the rhythms of this well-known song to make the music more your own. It's what jazz musicians do all the time!

Exercise 1, bars 9 – 16, is taken from the first part of the melody. Don't miss the quaver rest that begins each of the two phrases. The music begins after five crotchet clicks. Listen first as we play, then you repeat the music twice.

Exercise 1 (CD Track 34)

The music for exercise 2 is taken from the second part of the opening melody, bars 17 – 24, and begins after five crotchet clicks.

Exercise 2 (CD Track 35)

• There are many accidentals in this music, which require careful attention to intonation.
• Allow the music to build gradually between bars 37 – 55.
• The cue notes in bars 63 – 64 are optional.

8 Corcovado (Quiet Nights Of Quiet Stars)

- Play this piece in a quiet easy style.
Exercise 1, bars 12 – 19, is taken from the opening of the melody. The music begins after five crotchet clicks.
Listen first as we play, then you repeat the music twice.

Exercise 1 (CD track 36)

Exercise 2, bars 36 – 43, is taken from the close of the song, and begins after five crotchet clicks. Notice the first phrase of this extract begins with a quaver rest, but the following phrases begin with dotted crotchet rests.

Exercise 2 (CD Track 37)

- Notice that almost every phrase of this song begins with a quaver rest.
- There is much tied-note work in this piece, which calls for careful listening to our recording, as well as conscientious practice on your part.
- Follow the taps on the band track in the *rit.* at the end of the song to be sure of playing your final note at the correct moment.

9 Oye Como Va

- This piece is made up of several distinct melodies. Try and give each a musical character of its own.

Exercise 1, bars 5 – 12, is taken from the opening of the first melody. The music begins after four crotchet clicks. Listen first as we play, then you repeat the music twice.

Exercise 1 (CD Track 38)

Exercise 2, bars 27 – 34, is taken from the third melody. The music begins after four crotchet clicks.

Exercise 2 (CD Track 39)

- Pay attention to the accents, *staccato*, and *tenuto* markings.
- If you find the ties difficult, practise the music first without them. Reinstate the ties when you are more confident with the notes.
- The cue note in bar 42 is optional.
- The crotchet triplets in bar 64 are important. They cut across the rhythm of the piece with excitement. Listen to our recording if you are unsure how they are played.

10 The Girl from Ipanema

- The mood of this piece should be peaceful and relaxed.

Exercise 1, bars 5 – 12, is taken from the first part of the melody. The music begins after four crotchet clicks. Listen first as we play, then you repeat the music twice.

Exercise 1 (CD Track 40)

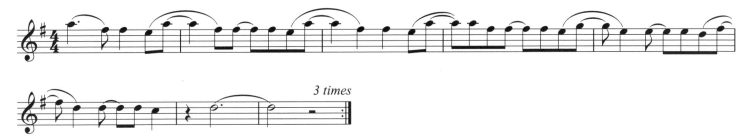

Exercise 2, bars 21 – 32, is taken from the middle section of the piece. Pay special attention to the accidentals. The music begins after four crotchet clicks.

Exercise 2 (CD Track 41)

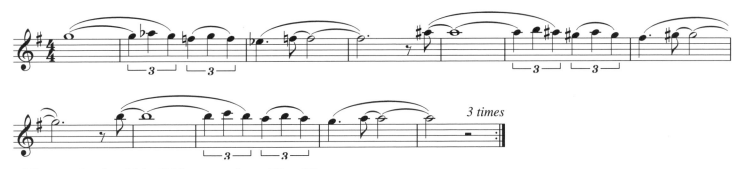

- The music should build between bars 21 – 33.
- Like much Latin American music, this piece uses triplet rhythms. Remember that the notes of the triplet should be rhythmically equal.

Bésame Mucho

Original Words & Music by Consuelo Velazquez
English Words by Sunny Skylar

Guantanamera

Words Adapted by Julian Orbon from a poem by José Marti
Music Adaptation by Pete Seeger & Julian Orbon

Tequila

Words & Music by Chuck Rio

Guaglione

By Giovanni Fanciulli & Nisa

Tempo di cha-cha

18

Mas Que Nada

Words & Music by Jorge Ben

Mas Que Nada

Words & Music by Jorge Ben

Bright beguine tempo

21

Mambo No. 5

Written by Perez 'Prez' Prado

Desafinado (Slightly Out Of Tune)

Original Words by Newton Mendonca
Music by Antonio Carlos Jobim
English Words by Jon Hendricks & Jessie Cavanaugh

Corcovado (Quiet Nights Of Quiet Stars)

Original Words & Music by Antonio Carlos Jobim
English Words by Gene Lees & Buddy Kaye

Oye Como Va

Words & Music by Tito Puente

The Girl From Ipanema

Original Words by Vinicius De Moraes
Music by Antonio Carlos Jobim
English Words by Norman Gimbel